In Which Era

WOULD YOU RATHER

Era

ERAS EDITION

With Over
130+
Questions...!

Published in 2023 by
Nyx Spectrum

In my
Would You Rather
Era

Questions...?
Taylor-themed Would You Rather

Welcome fellow Swifties to the Ultimate Taylor Swift-themed Would You Rather game for fans!

Each page of this book is filled with thought provoking and challenging Taylor Swift-themed questions that dive into the world of her music and the iconic influence she has had on the world.

Every Era of Taylor's evolving music journey is celebrated here. Spark new conversations and fun debates throughout this book...Are you ready for it?

Would you rather...

Get invited to one of Taylor's 4th of July parties in Rhode Island
OR
Take a private songwriting class taught by Taylor herself?

Would you rather...

Attend a concert where the crowd is silent and attentive
OR
Go to a show where everyone is screaming the lyrics and dancing wildly?

Would you rather...

Have Taylor Swift come out with a full makeup line
OR
Have Taylor Swift create an entire clothing store including different lines in the styles from all her Eras?

Would you rather...

Taylor release bonus tracks for *Lover*
OR
Have a full visual album the next time Taylor releases a new album?

WOULD YOU RATHER...

Live in an alternate world where Taylor Swift is now a
professional Opera Singer
OR
Live in a world where she is a famous painter?

WOULD YOU RATHER...

Visit Taylor's childhood home at the Christmas Tree Farm
OR
Visit the house her family lived in when they moved to Nashville
to start her career?

WOULD YOU RATHER...

Compete in a Super Smash Bros game with all the old and new
Taylors as characters to battle as
OR
Immerse yourself into the Sims were all the Taylors live under one
roof, and whom you can control like a god?

WOULD YOU RATHER...

Get to live at Holiday House through the year to maintain the
house while Taylor is away
OR
Get to live in her Nashville mansion while Taylor is away and
maintain that property for her?

Would You Rather...

Have Taylor go full cowgirl again with her next album
OR
Should Taylor's next album be Pirate-inspired?

Would You Rather...

Be able to relive a concert experience in a lucid dream over and over whenever you want
OR
Be awarded free front-row seats to the nearest concert venue for the rest of your life?

Would You Rather...

Have Taylor write songs that are even more honest and blunt about her life experiences
OR
Have Taylor start writing lyrics that are even more obscure and vague about her life than they already are?

Would You Rather...

Only get to converse with Taylor through social media for the next decade
OR
Only ever get to talk to her once in person for a whole hour?

WOULD YOU RATHER...

Become a part of Taylor's band that she tours with
OR
Become one of her backup dancers on tour?

WOULD YOU RATHER...

Have a fantastic romantic relationship with unfulfilling friendships
throughout your life
OR
Have an average romantic relationship with incredible
friendships?

WOULD YOU RATHER...

Swap cookie recipes with Taylor online
OR
Exchange cat pictures with Taylor over texts?

WOULD YOU RATHER...

Have your permanent style replicate Taylor's sparkly outfits in the
Bejeweled music video
OR
The plain clothing of "House Wench Taylor" in the *Bejeweled* music
video?

8

Would You Rather...

Have the ability to change your hairstyle in the blink of an eye

OR

Have the ability to change your entire closet's aesthetic with a nod of your head?

Would You Rather...

Experience a rain (or monsoon) show during one of Taylor's tours

OR

Experience the concert crowd creating a 2.3 or larger magnitude earthquake (aka Swift Quake)?

Would You Rather...

Have Taylor's next new album feature banjo-heavy music

OR

Have Taylor's next new album feature ukulele-heavy music?

Would You Rather...

Live in one of Taylor's many penthouses worldwide

OR

Live in one of her fantastic music video worlds?

would you rather...

Have Taylor's next album be Steampunk inspired
OR
Have her new album feature a Fantasy Astronomy vibe?

would you rather...

Ride next to Taylor in a getaway car
OR
Ride next to Taylor on a white horse?

would you rather...

Have every new Taylor album for the rest of her career be
endless summer sounding albums
OR
Let the rest of her career work be everlasting fall sounding
albums?

would you rather...

Have every new Taylor album for the rest of her career be eternal
spring sounding albums
OR
Have the rest of her career work be perpetual winter sounding
albums?

Would You Rather...

Have celebrities donate more money to major charities
OR
Help unknown budding artists with their influence to get their big start?

Would You Rather...

Listen to Classical instrumental versions of all of Taylor's songs
OR
Dance remixes of every song she's written?

Would You Rather...

Stand alone in defending your beliefs, facing criticism and isolation
OR
Compromise your values to be accepted by the majority?

Would You Rather...

Have Taylor only write about fictional people and relationships for the rest of her career
OR
Have Taylor only write autobiographical songs that reveal even more private details of her life?

would you rather...

Have your life narrated by a background soundtrack of all Taylor Swift songs
OR
Have your life narrated by Taylor Swift herself, but only you can hear her?

would you rather...

Have your favorite Taylor song go viral where it's so overplayed you begin to hate it
OR
Never get to hear your favorite song live on tour at all (or ever again)?

would you rather...

Be recognized by Taylor in public, getting a shoutout noticed by the world
OR
Have a secret signal with her, shared and noticed only between the two of you?

would you rather...

Be able to attend any one concert from the past
OR
Have guaranteed tickets for any one concert in the future?

would you rather...

Swap minds with Taylor Swift for a day
OR
Swap voices with Taylor Swift for a week?

would you rather...

Have the power to change one major event in Taylor's life, risking
the butterfly effect on the present
OR
be an observer of multiple events in her life, seeing the truth with
your own eyes but unable to change the outcome?

would you rather...

Always follow your heart, even if it means making difficult choices
OR
Always make the practical decision, even if it compromises your
own desires?

would you rather...

Be able to produce wings that appear like the *ME!* Mural in
Nashville from your back, but they can't fly
OR
Get to fly in Taylor's private jet for a round trip abroad once?

Would You Rather...?

Get a true old school Country album from Taylor
OR
Have a future album have a Gospel choir throughout?

Would You Rather...?

Live in a world where Taylor can weave dreams and nightmares for her fans
OR
Insert yourself consciously into other Taylor's dreams and nightmares as a bystander?

Would You Rather...?

See Taylor Swift switch into a new genre of music for the rest of her career
OR
Remain in the same style as her most recent album?

Would You Rather...?

Star in one of Taylor's music videos
OR
Be the first person to listen to a new album?

Would you rather...

Have the talent to write deeply emotional songs that touch millions but expose all of the most intimate details of your life
OR
Keep your privacy but never be able to express your deepest desires to anyone?

Would you rather...

Have "Bad Blood" with someone who has wronged you and hold that grudge
OR
"Shake it off" and move on with your life?

Would you rather...

Be given the opportunity to never grow up so you can retain your childhood creativity and innocence
OR
Embrace the complexities and challenges of adulthood?

Would you rather...

Write a song that becomes an anthem for heartbreak, knowing that you will constantly hear it and remind you of personal pain
OR
Write a one-hit wonder that becomes a viral sensation that gets super overplayed and overhyped?

WOULD YOU RATHER...

Get your heart broken constantly but also experience passionate love
OR
Never feel heartbreak because you never fall in love?

WOULD YOU RATHER...

Work on a project with Taylor, being seen as a professional peer
OR
Be a personal guest at a glamorous event, celebrating her latest achievement?

WOULD YOU RATHER...

Like to know who every Taylor Swift song is about and hear the stories behind each one
OR
Have her work become even more cryptic to continue her elaborate Easter egg hunt for the rest of her career?

WOULD YOU RATHER...

Meet Taylor Swift for twenty minutes
OR
Get free front-row tickets to each of her future tours?

Would You Rather...

Have one of her Eras Tour outfits custom-made for you by the designer

OR

Have one of her red carpet dresses made for you?

Would You Rather...

Read a series of novels by Taylor Swift based on "All Too Well"

OR

See her direct and produce a series on Netflix inspired by "betty"?

Would You Rather...

Wear outfits for the next 10 years all inspired by reputation

OR

Wear outfits for the next 10 years all inspired by Fearless?

Would You Rather...

Go on an elaborate social media scavenger hunt created by Taylor herself for her new music

OR

Try to solve a Swiftie-themed Escape Room that Taylor made, with your prize being your very own lifetime supply of concert tickets to her future shows?

WOULD YOU RATHER...

Be able to only listen to one album for the rest of your life
OR
Attend one concert per tour by your favorite artist?

WOULD YOU RATHER...

Go on a world tour with Taylor as a crew member
OR
Travel as a truck driver setting up her stages before she arrives?

WOULD YOU RATHER...

Only listen to music from the '70's
OR
Only new music that comes out 10 years from now?

WOULD YOU RATHER...

Have a song you wrote performed by Taylor Swift
OR
Record a duet with Taylor for her next album?

Would You Rather...

Listen to only live versions of Taylor's songs forever
OR
Only be able to listen to her Vault tracks for the rest of your life?

Would You Rather...

Have all your music on vinyl records to listen to
OR
Have all your music on mix tape cassettes to listen to?

Would You Rather...

Only be able to listen to music blasting through speakers
OR
Only be able to listen to music through headphones?

Would You Rather...

Get to pick the set list for Taylor's next tour
OR
Get to have one new song dedicated to you live on her next tour?

would you rather ...

Only be able to listen to the first half of every song
OR
Only be able to listen to the second half of any song?

would you rather ...

Have the ability to remember every lyric of every song you've
heard once
OR
Be able to play by ear any music you hear once?

would you rather ...

Have your favorite Taylor album never exist
OR
Have Taylor never tour again?

would you rather ...

Have your least favorite Taylor song stuck in your head forever
OR
Never be able to listen to your favorite Taylor song ever again?

Would You Rather...

Attend the Eras Tour with terrible seats but the best acoustics
OR
Have the best view but extremely poor sound quality?

Would You Rather...

Have Taylor return to her grunge phase of *reputation*
OR
Her cottagecore era of *folklore*?

Would You Rather...

See the Eras Tour in your home state/country
OR
Travel to attend the Eras Tour in a foreign country?

Would You Rather...

Have a backstage pass for every concert on tour but never get to see the show
OR
Have front-row tickets to your favorite show but no backstage access?

would you rather...

**Meet Taylor Swift's Mom
OR
Meet Taylor Swift's Best Friend?**

would you rather...

**Write music that gives people a sense of peace and comfort
OR
Inspire them to get up and make a positive change in their lives?**

would you rather...

**Have Taylor's next album feature an Academia aesthetic
OR
Futuristic style?**

would you rather...

**Be inducted to a Hall of Fame
OR
Win a Grammy for best new artist?**

would you rather...

Take up the hobby of making snow globes
OR
Take up knitting, creating a whole wardrobe of cardigans?

would you rather...

Dress up like Hipsters with Taylor and her friends
OR
Dress up in fairytale ballgowns for a night on the town with Taylor?

would you rather...

Send messages with your wardrobe like Taylor Swift
OR
Only be able to communicate online with cryptic emojis?

would you rather...

Be able to perform the whole Eras Tour dance routines from start to finish
OR
Get to dive under the Eras Tour stage like Taylor?

Would You Rather...?

Go to a Chiefs football game in hopes of seeing Taylor
OR
Go to an Ed Sheeran concert hoping that she will be the surprise guest?

Would You Rather...?

Get to ride the giant Caticorn of Olivia everywhere
OR
Ride the robot White Horse from the _...Ready for it?_ music video everywhere?

Would You Rather...?

Decorate your space like the 70's glam of Midnights
OR
Redecorate your space with the vibes of evermore?

Would You Rather...?

Have another big city sounding album from Taylor
OR
Another deep woods album?

Would you rather...

Get the "mistake" album Woodvale released
OR
Find out all of Taylor's other potential pen names besides the deceased Nils Sjöberg?

Would you rather...

Rock body glitter and hair gems to the next concert
OR
Faded blue jeans and cowboy boots to Taylor's next tour?

Would you rather...

Have Taylor announce a Vault Song Tour
OR
Get a full Music Video Album of one of her past works?

Would you rather...

Have "not a lot going on at the moment"
OR
Have to make a friendship bracelet for every person in one of the Eras Tour stadiums?

WOULD YOU RATHER...

Be tracked down by Taylor to take a selfie together
OR
Have Taylor write a song about you?

WOULD YOU RATHER...

Have Taylor's next style be Barbie-inspired
OR
Have her next style be Mermaid-inspired?

WOULD YOU RATHER...

Receive cookies baked by Taylor herself on Valentine's Day
OR
Get relationship advice from Taylor herself?

WOULD YOU RATHER...

Have a playlist created for you personally by Taylor
OR
Be invited to one of her homes for a listening party?

Would You Rather...

See a full length movie trilogy created by Taylor Swift
OR
Attend Taylor Swift the Musical on Broadway?

Would You Rather...

Listen to a Metal album from Taylor
OR
Jam out to a Blues Album from Taylor?

Would You Rather...

Have Taylor release *Lover (Deluxe Version)* with new songs
OR
Have her release the *Evermore: Long Pond Studio Sessions?*

Would You Rather...

Have the Eras Tour Surprise song piano as a centerpiece in your home
OR
Her moss-covered Eras tour piano?

WOULD YOU RATHER...

Have a mug that reads "I'm just like DAMN, it's 7am."
OR
Have a mug that is reserved just for "Swiftea"?

WOULD YOU RATHER...

Bake cookies on December 13th in honor of Taylor's birthday
OR
Have all of your holiday decorations be Taylor themed?

WOULD YOU RATHER...

Hang out with Taylor at 2am
OR
Spend time with Taylor during daylight hours?

WOULD YOU RATHER...

When asked for advice, you can only speak in Taylor Swift lyrics
OR
Only be able to recite Taylor Swift lyrics when asked
what time it is?

Would You Rather...

Get a makeover done in the style of *1989*
OR
Have your makeover inspired by *Speak Now?*

Would You Rather...

Be able to travel back in time to mend a past regret
OR
Settle a score Bad Blood style?

Would You Rather...

Get your face painted for your next concert with a
theme inspired by *Red*
OR
Get your face painted in the style of *Fearless?*

Would You Rather...

Bring back country music and have a Debut Tour
OR
Do a whole tour just with folklore and evermore songs?

would you rather...

Go back in time to see the Red Tour
OR
Reverse time to see the Speak Now World Tour?

would you rather...

Go back in time to see the 1989 Tour
OR
reputation Tour?

would you rather...

Bring Lover Fest back from the dead
OR
Bring the Eras Tour around again?

would you rather...

Wear subtle Taylor Swift themed items only true fans will know
references to
OR
Wear Taylor merch with her face all over it that makes it obvious
you're a Taylor Swift fan?

Would You Rather...

Use *1989* as your go-to workout album to play from start to finish
OR
Listen to the entirety of *reputation* to pump you up and make you sweat?

Would You Rather...

Get a Reggae EP from Taylor
OR
Listen to an Indie Rock EP from Taylor?

Would You Rather...

Have a license plate frame that reads "nothing good starts in a getaway car"
OR
Hang a pair of dice from your rear view mirror with a tag that reads "In this car we listen to Taylor's Version"?

Would You Rather...

Welcome people into your home with a doormat that reads:
"This is our place, we make the rules"
OR
"I hope you like Taylor Swift"?

would you rather...

**Have Taylor Swift's song *Lover*
OR
Enchanted as your first dance at your wedding?**

would you rather...

**Have *invisible string*
OR
This Love playing softly as you walk down the aisle at your wedding?**

would you rather...

**Play *Paper Rings*
OR
Starlight at your wedding reception?**

would you rather...

**Play *End Game*
OR
Everything Has Changed at your Engagement Party?**

would you rather...

Have your favorite album also be your favorite fashion era
OR
Have your favorite album have a complete style makeover?

would you rather...

Be besties with Junior Jewels Taylor
OR
Be friends with cardigan Taylor?

would you rather...

Hang out with reputation Taylor
OR
Reminisce with zombie Taylor?

would you rather...

Have more collaboration songs with Taylor and other artists
OR
Should she keep going solo because her songs are better on her own?

Would You Rather...?

Visit Cornelia Street and walk by her old apartment, leaving
flowers at the doorstep
OR
Visit the bench now dedicated to her in Centennial Park and enjoy
a quiet afternoon?

Would You Rather...?

Have Taylor exclusively dress in an Old Hollywood style
OR
Have her dress completely in a Punk style?

Would You Rather...?

Write "It's me, Hi, I'm the Grad, it's me" on your graduation cap
OR
"I gave my blood, sweat, and tears for this" on top of your
graduation hat?

Would You Rather...?

Only listen to vault songs from Taylor's albums
OR
Only listen to the remixes from her albums?

Would you rather...

Have Taylor Swift sing a duet with Harry Styles
OR
Have Taylor sing a duet with Matty Healy?

Would you rather...

Have Taylor free-style rap her entire next album
OR
From now on, every new Taylor album for the rest of her career
will be Rock albums?

Would you rather...

Have Taylor put out Taylor's Version of another Christmas Album
OR
Do a complete Acoustic Album of her newest work?

Would you rather...

Live without the whole *reputation* album
OR
Live without her *Red* album?

WOULD YOU RATHER...

Never listen to *Lover* album again
OR
Never listen to *1989* album again?

WOULD YOU RATHER...

Only listen to Taylor's *Fearless* Album
OR
Only get to listen to her *Speak Now* album?

WOULD YOU RATHER...

Never listen to *folklore* again
OR
Never listen to her *evermore* album again?

WOULD YOU RATHER...

Have *Now that We Don't Talk* be a longer song
OR
Have a longer version of the song *gold rush*?

Would You Rather...

Listen to an extended version of *Midnight Rain*
OR
this is me trying?

Would You Rather...

Have Taylor's *State of Grace* song shortened
OR
Condense the song *happiness?*

Would You Rather...

Have extended versions of the vault songs from *1989 (Taylor's Version)*
OR
Shortened songs on Taylor's Version of her *Speak Now* album?

Would You Rather...

Only be able to listen to *Debut, Red, Evermore, Lover* and *Midnights*
OR
Speak Now, Fearless, 1989, reputation and *folklore?*

WOULD YOU RATHER...

Listen to all the existing unreleased vault tracks and choose which one will get to be released as Taylor's Version
OR
Be able to select the concept for Taylor's next new album – including sound, themes, fashion, and aesthetics?

WOULD YOU RATHER...

Never be able to listen to your favorite Taylor album again
OR
Never be able to listen to any new music released after *Midnights?*

WOULD YOU RATHER...

Write songs with a glitter gel pen
OR
Write songs with a quill and ink?

WOULD YOU RATHER...

Switch places right now and live Taylor Swift's lifestyle
OR
Become someone close to Taylor Swift in her personal life?

Would you rather…

Only be able to listen to the 13th song on each of Taylor's Albums
OR
Only be able to listen to the 1st song on every album?

No. 13

Invisible
Change
Last Kiss
The Lucky One
Clean
This Is Why We Can't Have Nice Things
I Forgot That You Existed
epiphany
marjorie
Mastermind

No. 1

Tim McGraw
Fearless
Mine
State of Grace
Welcome to New York
…Ready for it?
False God
the 1
willow
Lavender Haze

Would you rather...

Only be able to listen to the 5th song on each of Taylor's albums

OR

Only be able to listen to the 7th song on each of her albums?

No. 5

Cold As You
White Horse
Dear John
All Too Well
All You Had To Do Was Stay
Delicate
The Archer
my tears ricochet
tolerate it
You're On Your Own, Kid

No. 7

Tied Together With A Smile
Breathe
The Story of Us
I Almost Do
I Wish You Would
So It Goes...
Miss Americana & The Heartbreak Prince
seven
happiness
Question...?

Would you rather...

Only listen to Taylor's Glitter Gel Pen songs
OR
Only listen to her Fountain Pen songs?

Bejeweled
Karma
I Forgot That You Existed
We Are Never Getting Back Together
You Belong With Me
I Think He Knows
London Boy
You Need To Calm Down
Jump Then Fall
22
Today Was A Fairytale
Hey Stephen
Afterglow

Lavender Haze
Maroon
You're On Your Own, Kid
Midnight Rain
Labyrinth
Sweet Nothing
Question...?
False God
Cruel Summer
exile
the 1
betty
champagne problems
marjorie
Lover
The Archer
Cornelia Street
White Horse
right where you left me
Treacherous
long story short
All Too Well
State of Grace
I Almost Do
Holy Ground

Would you rather...

Only listen to Taylor's Quill Pen songs
OR
Never again listen to any of her Quill Pen songs?

Anti-Hero
Snow On The Beach
Mastermind
ivy
hoax
my tears ricochet
epiphany
the last great American dynasty
peace
willow
tolerate it
happiness
Red
Carolina
evermore
cowboy like me
Sad Beautiful Tragic

Tied Together With A Theme

Playlist Era

Dear Reader, in this chapter, you have to make the unimaginable choice of choosing which Taylor playlist is a better soundtrack for certain scenerios.

*Bonus Tip - Enhance your experience by listening to these playlists while reading through the rest of this book.

(Don't blame me if this book sparks lively debates!)

Which playlist would you rather blast in your getaway car?

Tim McGraw
Change
The Story of Us
Red
Out of the Woods
Look What You Made Me Do
Cruel Summer
the 1
right where you left me
Anti-Hero

OR

Mary's Song
Jump Then Fall
Haunted
State of Grace
I Know Places
Getaway Car
Afterglow
august
gold rush
You're On Your Own, Kid

Which playlist would you rather listen to while drift off to sleep after midnight?

New Year's Day
Never Grow Up
Come Back...Be Here
Wildest Dreams
Breathe
peace

OR

You Are In Love
Treacherous
Begin Again
The Archer
Clean
Everything Has Changed

Which playlist would you rather to go running wild to or hit the gym with?

Picture to Burn
You Belong With Me
Better Than Revenge
Holy Ground
Style
Bad Blood
Death By A Thousand Cuts
invisible string
ivy
Bejeweled

OR

Should've Said No
Forever & Always
Sparks Fly
Red
Wonderland
...Ready for it?
The Man
the great american dynasty
long story short
Karma

Which playlist would you rather get cozy and listen to during the holidays?

Snow on the Beach
exile
Back to December
this is me trying
Cold As You
evermore

OR

Lover
Christmas Tree Farm
Forever Winter
tis the damn season
New Year's Day
mirrorball

Which playlist would you rather put on when you're in need of a good cry?

Tied Together With A Smile
Breathe
Dear John
The Moment I Knew
Soon You'll Get Better
exile
happiness
Bigger Than The Whole Sky
High Infidelity

OR

Teardrops on my Guitar
White Horse
Back to December
Ronan
Nothing New
tolerate it
illicit affairs
Maroon
You're Not Sorry

Which playlist would you rather dance wildly to?

22
Karma
Welcome to New York
Getaway Car
Dancing With Our Hands Tied
You Belong With Me
New Romantics

OR

Bejeweled
Paper Rings
Mr. Perfectly Fine
I Know Places
I Can See You
ME!
Holy Ground

Which playlist would you rather listen to while you're healing from a tough day?

Innocent
Clean
Holy Ground
A Place In This World
Change
Begin Again
Daylight
The Very First Night

OR

this is me trying
happiness
It's Time to Go
Breathe
evermore
I Almost Do
Long Live
The Archer

Which playlist would you rather scream to at the top of your lungs at your haters?

Shake It Off
I Forgot That You Existed
Mean
Look What You Made Me Do
You Need to Calm Down
Tell Me Why
Anti-Hero

OR

Vigilante Shit
no body, no crime
Call it What You Want
Blank Space
mad woman
I Did Something Bad
This Is Why We Can't Have Nice Things

Which playlist would you rather declare as Taylor's "Essential Love Songs"?

Love Story
Lover
Our Song
Paris
This Love
invisible string
Sweet Nothing
Fearless
You Belong With Me
Today Was A Fairytale

OR

Paper Rings
Hey Stephen
The Very First Night
Run
You Are In Love
Starlight
Dress
King of My Heart
Enchanted
Treacherous

Which playlist would you rather claim as your "Wake up & Smell the Breakup" mixtape?

The Story of Us
The Way I Loved You
Last Kiss
Holy Ground
Would've, Could've, Should've
Picture to Burn
Hits Different
champagne problems
Cornelia Street
cowboy like me

OR

Death By A Thousand Cuts
right where you left me
Clean
the 1
Dear John
We Are Never Getting Back Together
Miss Americana & The Heartbreak Prince
Is It Over Now?
Babe
Fifteen

Which playlist would you rather tune out the world with headphones while you focus on important work?

"Slut!"
Clean
cardigan
august
Snow On The Beach
This Love
All Of The Girls You Loved Before
Nothing New
Delicate
champagne problems
Mastermind

OR

The Archer
ephiphany
peace
New Year's Day
Dear Reader
Glitch
All Too Well (10 Minute Version)
ivy
happiness
seven
mirrorball

Which playlist would you rather sing in the shower before you think you're finally clean?

Don't Blame Me
Stay Stay Stay
The Lucky One
The Man
When Emma Falls in Love
Question...?

OR

Lavender Haze
I Knew You Were Trouble
Enchanted
I Think He Knows
Gorgeous
The Last Time
Speak Now
I Can See You

Which playlist would you rather crown the title of "Ultimate Deep Cuts" from each of Taylor's albums?

A Perfectly Good Heart
The Otherside Of The Door
Innocent
The Last Time
This Love
Dancing With Our Hands Tied
False God
hoax
coney island
Dear Reader

OR

Invisible
Tell Me Why
Ours
Girl At Home
New Romantics
So It Goes...
It's Nice To Have A Friend
peace
marjorie
Glitch

No Bad Blood

Song vs Song Era

This chapter can be played as a lightning round where each fan must make swift choices to reveal their favored songs. Or if given an impossible choice, spark a friendly debate to find out why which song should be crowned the winner...?

???????????????
Taylor Swift

0:13   -1:30

Would you rather listen to...

Anti-Hero OR Don't Blame Me?

Cruel Summer OR Karma?

Blank Space OR Paper Rings?

Hits Different OR I Can See You?

Love Story OR Enchanted?

1:30

-0:13

Would you rather listen to...

We Are Never Getting Back Together
OR
Picture to Burn?

I Did Something Bad
OR
I Knew You Were Trouble?

Lover OR King of My Heart?

Mean
OR
This Is Why We Can't Have Nice Things?

Is It Over Now? OR gold rush?

0:13   -1:30

Would you rather listen to...

Cardigan OR Last Kiss?

the 1 OR New Year's Day?

long story short OR Wonderland?

Maroon OR invisible string?

State of Grace OR Innocence?

1:30 -0:13

Would you rather listen to...

Style OR The Moment I Knew?

Back to December OR Come Back...Be Here?

Clean OR Tear Drops On My Guitar?

The Archer OR tolerate it?

**White Horse
OR
Death By A Thousand Cuts?**

0:13

-1:30

Would you rather listen to...

Haunted OR right where you left me?

Mastermind OR august?

Holy Ground OR willow?

Vigilante Shit OR no body, no crime?

Tim McGraw OR cowboy like me?

1:30 -0:13

62

Would you rather listen to...

High Infidelity OR illicit affairs?

**Starlight
OR
All You Had To Do Was Stay?**

Mine OR Red?

**Miss Americana & The Heartbreak Prince
OR
How You Get The Girl?**

The Man OR mad woman?

0:13   -1:30

Would you rather listen to...

New Romantics OR Nothing New?

Midnight Rain OR my tears ricochet?

Labyrinth OR Call It What You Want?

betty OR Forever & Always?

Daylight OR Lavender Haze?

1:30 -0:13

Would you rather listen to...

Delicate OR Sweet Nothing?

22 OR Bejeweled?

mirrorball OR Snow On The Beach?

Cornelia Street OR champagne problems?

**Dear John
OR
Would've, Could've, Should've?**

0:13   -1:30

Would you rather listen to...

Question...? OR Treacherous?

Fifteen OR London Boy?

Love Story OR This Love?

Sad Beautiful Tragic OR Cold As You?

Last Kiss OR The Great War?

1:30   -0:13

Would you rather listen to...

So It Goes OR Afterglow?

Should've Said No OR I Think He Knows?

All of the Girls You Loved Before OR "Slut!"?

Invisible OR Untouchable?

The Lucky One OR The Best Day?

0:13

-1:30

Would you rather listen to...

Welcome to New York
OR
last great american dynasty?

Starlight OR Wildest Dreams?

Gorgeous OR Stay Beautiful?

I Think He Knows OR Treacherous?

I Almost Do OR A Place In This World?

1:30   -0:13

Would you rather listen to...

Getaway Car OR Babe?

Mary's Song OR Stay Stay Stay?

Soon You'll Get Better
OR
Bigger Than The Whole Sky?

Mr. Perfectly Fine OR The Last Time?

Out of the Woods
OR
I Forgot That You Existed?

0:13 -1:30

Would you rather listen to...

**Sparks Fly
OR
I Knew You Were Trouble?**

Glitch OR I Know Places?

Our Song OR Hey Stephen?

You Belong With Me OR Paris?

**Long Live
OR
All Too Well (10 Minute Version)?**

1:30   -0:13

Would've Could've Should've

Lost Music Videos Era

Taylor has a reputation for her beautifully cryptic music videos, each a treasure trove of stories and hidden Easter eggs. Which of her songs do you find yourself longing for a music videos of...?

WOULD YOU RATHER WATCH A MUSIC VIDEO FOR...?

Getaway Car
OR
Miss Americana & The Heartbreak Prince?

Labyrinth OR Wonderland?

You're On Your Own, Kid OR Mary's Song?

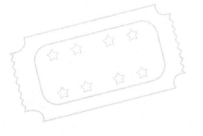

Dancing With Our Hands Tied OR You All Over Me?

WOULD YOU RATHER WATCH A MUSIC VIDEO FOR...?

Daylight OR State of Grace?

I Think He Knows OR Gorgeous?

Cruel Summer OR mirrorball?

Sparks Fly OR Sad Beautiful Tragic?

WOULD YOU RATHER WATCH A MUSIC VIDEO FOR...?

I Did Something Bad OR Dress?

The Lucky One OR This Love?

Mastermind OR Paper Rings?

Question...? OR Don't Blame Me?

WOULD YOU RATHER WATCH A MUSIC VIDEO FOR...?

right where you left me OR Haunted?

White Horse OR Snow on the Beach?

The Archer OR august?

Mr. Perfectly Fine OR champagne problems?

WOULD YOU RATHER WATCH A MUSIC VIDEO FOR...?

Clean OR Starlight?

The Story of Us OR New Year's Day?

the lakes OR marjorie?

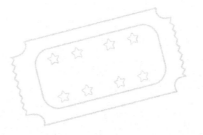

Sweet Nothing OR Death By A Thousand Cuts?

WOULD YOU RATHER WATCH A MUSIC VIDEO FOR...?

Dear John OR Now That We Don't Talk?

seven OR 'tis the damn season?

coney island OR Cornelia Street?

gold rush OR Nothing New?

WOULD YOU RATHER WATCH A MUSIC VIDEO FOR...?

happiness OR Back to December?

Enchanted OR cowboy like me?

mad woman OR the last great american dynasty?

ivy OR Paris?

WOULD YOU RATHER WATCH A MUSIC VIDEO FOR...?

Labyrinth OR I Think He Knows?

Maroon OR This Is Why We Can't Have Nice Things?

Holy Ground OR Message In A Bottle?

The Great War OR Long Live?

Check out our other books!

Made in United States
Orlando, FL
08 February 2024

43468553R00046